DIS<del>CARD</del>

THE WAY OF DANGER

The Story of Theseus

Ian Serraillier

THE WAY OF DANGER

The Story of Theseus

Illustrated by

WILLIAM STOBBS

New York

HENRY Z. WALCK, INCORPORATED

1963

First published by Oxford University Press, London 1962
First American Edition 1963
© Ian Serraillier 1962
Library of Congress Catalog Card Number: 63-10911
PRINTED IN THE UNITED STATES OF AMERICA

To
ANDREW

Acknowledgements

The author is grateful for the valuable help and guidance he has received from the following books:

Leonard Cottrell: THE BULL OF MINOS

(Holt, Rinehart and Winston, Inc.)

Trans. Sir J. G. Frazer: APOLLODORUS *(Heinemann)*

Robert Graves: THE GREEK MYTHS *(Penguin Books)*

C. Kerenyi: THE GODS OF THE GREEKS *(Grove Press, Inc.)*

C. Kerenyi: THE HEROES OF THE GREEKS *(Grove Press, Inc.)*

Ovid, trans. F. J. Miller: METAMORPHOSES *(Heinemann)*

Plutarch, trans. Bernadotte Perrin: PLUTARCH'S LIVES

(Heinemann)

M. Rostovtzeff: A HISTORY OF THE ANCIENT WORLD

(Oxford University Press)

J. C. Stobart: THE GLORY THAT WAS GREECE

(Sidgwick and Jackson)

Rex Warner: MEN AND GODS *(MacGibbon and Kee)*

Contents

1 THE SECRET OF THE ROCK

AITHRA said to her son on his sixteenth birthday, 'Go into the field, Theseus, and lift the rock at the foot of the olive-tree and bring me what lies underneath.'

Obediently he ran to the rock and tore away the smothering weeds and ivy and tried to lift it. Soon he came back to his mother all hot and breathless and

1

said, 'It is too heavy for me, mother. Why do you ask me to lift it?'

'It was your father's wish,' said Aithra.

'What do I care for his wishes?' said Theseus. 'I have never seen him. I have never heard his name, for no one speaks of him here. All I know of my family is that you are a princess, the daughter of Pittheus, King of Troezen, where we live. He told me once that I had in my veins the blood of Poseidon, the sea-god whom our people worship. Is he my father?'

'You are descended from the sea-god, but he is not your father.'

'Then who is my father?'

'When you can lift the stone I will tell you about him and your own destiny. Be patient till then.'

And Aithra, who had been named after the cloudless sky, calmed his passionate spirit, for the boy had none of his mother's serenity. Yet he was brave and self-reliant. Once, when he was only seven, the great Heracles had dined at the palace. He had taken off the lion-skin he wore and thrown it on to a stool. When the palace children came in, they thought it was a real lion and ran away screaming. Theseus ran away with them, but not because he was afraid. He had gone to fetch an axe from the wood-pile to kill the lion. As well as courage he had ambition and much wisdom for his years. Now he saw that if he was to lift the rock and know his destiny he must also be strong. So he spent his days wrestling and boxing, riding and racing, taming horses, hunting the bull and the wild boar, and chasing the deer over the hills, till he was the strongest youth in the land.

When a full year had passed, he was ready to test his strength again, but he could not shift the stone then, nor the year after. Yet all this time he was gaining in strength and skill and also learning a measure of patience. Meanwhile his mother taught him not to squander his powers, but to set his mind to all that was brave and useful and true.

On his nineteenth birthday she sent him once more to lift the rock. Putting his arms round it, he took a deep breath and heaved with all his might. He tried a second time and a third without success. Then he put his shoulder to it and pushed hard—and felt it move.

'Next time I shall succeed,' he said, 'even if my heart bursts inside me.'

Again he put his shoulder to the rock and eased it up and up an inch at a time, and then with a great surge of energy and a sudden twist rolled it over. On the ground lay a pair of sandals and a bronze sword with an ivory hilt. There was a small hollow at the base of the rock just large enough to hold them.

3

He picked them up and ran to find his mother.

Off Troezen there is a small island so near the shore that you can wade barefoot to it. The temple of Athene stood here, and Aithra liked to sit on the steps and look out over the bay to the purple mountains of Aegina and the Attic shore beyond. She had finished her prayers and was sitting here when Theseus came splashing through the water, shouting that he had lifted the rock. She ran to meet him, and when she saw what was in his hands she smothered him with kisses.

4

While he tried on the sandals, she was trembling. They fitted so well that they might have been made for him. Then she took the sword from him and showed him the figure carved on the ivory hilt—a serpent twined round an olive.

'This is the sign of Kecrops, the heroic founder of Athens, who was half man, half serpent. You are descended from him,' she told him. 'Some weeks before you were born your father hid the sword and the sandals under the rock. He told me that, if you were a boy, as soon as you reached manhood and could move the rock, I was to send you to him. He said you were to take the sword and the sandals with you.'

'What is my father's name?' said Theseus.

'Aegeus.'

'And where does he live?'

Aithra pointed across the bay. 'You see the island of Aegina,' she said. 'Beyond it lies Athens, the noblest city in Greece. The soil is not hard and barren as it is here, but rich in crops. Your father is King of Athens, and you are his son and heir to his throne.'

Theseus was silent for a minute.

Then his mother said, 'The time has come for you to leave me. Go in secret and tell no one of your journey, for the fifty sons of Pallas have been plotting to steal his throne. If they knew you were his son, they would kill you.'

'And may I not take you with me, mother?' said Theseus.

Aithra sighed and hid her eyes from him. 'Your father has asked for you alone, not for me. I would give all I have to go with you, but I dare not disobey him. You must find a ship in the morning and sail across the bay.'

'The voyage is too easy,' said Theseus. 'I would rather go by land, round by the Isthmus.'

'No, not that way!' his mother begged. 'You will be killed by robbers and bandits.'

'You are wrong, mother. *I* shall kill *them*—as my uncle Heracles would if he had the chance. I have my father's sword—how can I fail?'

'No traveller who took that road has ever reached Athens alive,' said Aithra.

'Then I will be the first,' said Theseus. 'If I can bring my father proof of my manhood, he will honour me and love me all the more.'

Aithra did not dissuade him. Her son was no longer a boy but a man, and he knew his mind.

2 THE MAN WITH THE IRON CLUB,
AND THE PINE-BENDER

In the morning Theseus put on his sandals, his purple tunic, and a soft woollen cloak, and buckled his father's sword to his side. Then he said good-bye to his mother and set off along the coast road to Athens.

He had not gone far when the lace of one of his sandals came undone. As he stooped to tie it up, he heard a loud swishing sound close to his head. He looked up and saw a huge bulky fellow standing over him and waving an iron club. This was Periphetes, the man with the iron club. He used to hide among the rocks till a traveller came by and then, if he tried to pass, spring upon him and beat out his brains with the club. If Theseus had not stooped to tie his lace at that very moment, that would have been the end of him, for Periphetes had had plenty of practice and his aim was sure. Theseus had time to jump aside.

'My father gave me this club—my father Hephaistos, the god of fire. He forged it himself in the Black Mountains,' said Periphetes, as he prepared to strike again. 'You will not escape it a second time.'

Again the iron club swished through the air. But Theseus was nimble on his feet and dodged again. Periphetes was slow and clumsy, for he had inherited weak ankles from his father and he limped. His strength was in his arms.

Never before had Periphetes missed twice. His temper crackled like the fire in his father's forge. Then with both hands he whirled the club in the air. But Theseus had drawn his sword and struck at the man's wrist, so the club fell clattering on to the stones.

8

Theseus snatched it up and, while Periphetes was still stumbling to his feet, quickly finished him off. Then, taking the club with him, he went on his way, leaving the body to the wolves and ravens.

Near Corinth the road turns off to the Isthmus and only a narrow strip of land separates two seas. There is a pinewood here, and on stormy days the wind blows in from the seas, howling and groaning among the branches. This was the sound that Theseus heard as he came to the edge of the wood. Yet no storm was blowing; the sea was blue and quiet and the air was still—where did the noise come from?

Suddenly he stopped still.

'Stranger, help me to bend this tree,' said a deep voice quite near. 'I cannot manage it alone.'

A stone's throw away from Theseus was the tallest man he had ever seen. With his head tucked up among the branches and both arms outstretched, he was tugging at the top of a pine-tree, and rivers of sweat were running down his back. The trunk bent like an archer's bow and the roots began to crack. When he had pulled the top to just within Theseus's reach, he called out, 'Boy, hold on to this tree!'

'Why should I?' said Theseus.

'Because it blocks the road and travellers cannot get by. So does the next one to it. We must uproot them both. Hold on to it while I see to the other.'

'I know that trick,' said Theseus. 'As soon as I catch hold of it you will tie my hands to it. Then you will bend down the other tree and tie my legs to that and let go. I do not wish to be torn to pieces.'

'What makes you think so badly of me?' asked the man, still holding on to the tree.

'I know who you are,' said Theseus. 'You are Sinis, the pine-bender, and that is how you treat everyone who tries to pass. You will not do the same to me.'

'We shall see,' said the man, and he let go of the tree. As it sprang upright, there was a great tearing of leaves and a wrenching and cracking of branches, and all the birds for miles around splashed up in terror from the wood and flew away.

Sinis reached down with his cruel hands to grab at Theseus and wrestle with him, but Theseus dodged and caught him round the knees so that he over-balanced and fell. Then he sprang upon Sinis and they rolled over and over in the mud and the fallen leaves. Sinis tried to crush him with his arms, but Theseus wriggled out of his grasp and leapt up. While Sinis was still lumbering to his feet, Theseus stunned him with his club. He tied his legs to the arched pine-tree and bent down the other tree and tied his arms to that. Then he released both trees at the same time.

So Sinis met the fate he deserved.

And Theseus crossed the Isthmus safely and continued his journey.

3 SKIRON THE BRIGAND, AND THE
FAMOUS BED

THE road which led to the Isthmus was no more than
a rough mule track, and the most dangerous spot was
the bend at the foot of the Crane Mountain. Here the
rocks rose very steeply, and on the left a precipice

plunged down to the sea. Sometimes an avalanche of stones would block the path. Then the traveller had to climb down to the sea and walk along the narrow beach till it ended. After that he had to wade or swim to the place where he could climb up again to the mule track. Luckily for Theseus the path was clear today.

Soon he met a man with wild eyes and wild clothes sitting on a rock, with a bronze bowl full of water beside him. This was Skiron the brigand, and it was he who kept the path clear.

'You may not pass until you have paid me the toll,' said Skiron.

'I have no money,' said Theseus.

'You do not need money. You simply pay me by stooping to wash my feet in this bowl.'

'Is the sea-turtle hungry today, then?' said Theseus.

'What sea-turtle?' said Skiron angrily. 'I don't understand you.'

But he understood very well. As soon as a traveller stooped to wash his feet, he would kick him over the cliff into the sea, where a giant sea-turtle that ate nothing but men was swimming about, waiting to eat him.

'If you look over the cliff, you will see the turtle waiting,' said Theseus.

'And the moment my back is turned, you will push

me over,' said Skiron. 'My wits are not as dim as you think. I tell you, there is no turtle there.'

'You are quite right,' said Theseus. 'Before I climbed up here, I went down to the water and cut off its head with my sword.'

'What!' said Skiron, and he turned and peered over the edge of the cliff.

At once Theseus picked up the bowl, hurled it at his head and knocked him over. Skiron turned six somersaults in the air and hit the water with a loud smack. A huge fountain of white spray rose into the air. When it had subsided, Theseus saw the giant sea-turtle break the surface and plunge down after Skiron for his last meal of human flesh.

Theseus was by now very tired, and, when some hours later he met a young man who offered him a bed for the night, he gladly accepted.

'My master Procrustes is most hospitable,' said the young man, 'and he loves to have a guest under his roof. He is lonely and enjoys hearing tales of foreign parts.'

'I am too tired to tell stories tonight,' said Theseus.

'They will keep till the morning. You shall have something to eat and then go straight to bed. My master's bed is famous—there is no other one like it in the world, for it fits every guest perfectly, no matter

14

how tall or short he is. And you will sleep on it as you never slept before.'

It was almost dark when they came to a river. They were walking along the bank towards the bridge, when suddenly the servant missed his footing and fell in. He shouted for help, but the torrent quickly swept him away.

Theseus dropped his club and ran along the bank downstream till he saw him, thrashing about helplessly in the foaming water. He jumped in, seized him under the arms, and dragged him ashore.

To judge from his coughing and spluttering, the servant seemed to have swallowed half the river. When he had at last recovered his breath, he astonished Theseus by telling him that he must not on any account come to the house with him.

'Why not?' asked Theseus.

'Because you have saved my life, and now I want to save yours. If you lie down on my master's bed, you will never wake up again. If you are too long for it, he will lop off your legs till they are short enough; if you are too short, he will stretch your limbs till they are long enough. He treats all his guests in this way. I am the only one who fitted the bed exactly and he has kept me as his servant ever since. Hurry now and go back the way you came.'

But it was too late for Theseus to go back even if he had wanted to, for a lantern came bobbing towards them in the darkness, and the man who was carrying it was Procrustes. He had heard his servant shouting for help and had come out to see what was the matter.

'I fell into the torrent and this stranger saved me,' the servant explained.

'I shall be glad to reward him with a meal and a good night's rest,' said Procrustes. 'And while he's asleep, we can dry his clothes by the fire.'

'He is in a hurry to get to Corinth,' said the servant.

But Procrustes would take no refusal. He gripped Theseus by the arm and brought him to his house, which was just over the bridge. It was built of rough-hewn stones, and a wild fig-tree grew by the door. Inside a log fire was blazing—there was no other light in the room—and there was a sheep roasting on the spit and jugs of wine on the table.

While the servant prepared the meal, Procrustes and Theseus sat down at the table and sipped the wine. Theseus looked at his host's blue gown and all the gold and silver bracelets on his arms and wondered how many travellers like himself he had robbed and killed. Then he glanced over his shoulder and saw among the shadows the two wooden posts at the foot of the famous bed.

They ate the meal in silence, and when it was over Procrustes said, 'You must be very tired after your journey.' And he showed him the bed.

'It looks too long for me,' said Theseus.

'I will make sure that it fits you,' said Procrustes. 'Just lie down and you'll see.'

'I hate sleeping in wet clothes,' said Theseus. 'I thought you said you would dry them for me.'

'Ah yes, so I did. I will fetch you a tunic,' said Procrustes.

While he was gone from the room to fetch the tunic, Theseus had a word with the servant, who was busy clearing the table. Then he undressed, and when Procrustes brought in the tunic, he put it on and lay down on the bed.

At once Procrustes seized his ankles and fastened them with leather straps to the posts at the foot of the bed. Meanwhile the servant, who knew what to do, tied each wrist with a strap and fastened them—or, rather, pretended to fasten them—to posts at the head of the bed. When Procrustes, on his way to attend to the stretching-gear, was within reach, Theseus grabbed him round the waist with both arms and shouted to the servant to cut the straps on his feet. Next moment they were wrestling together in the firelight, while on the walls and the ceiling their

shadows wrestled like black giants. They knocked over the table. They hurtled into a wine jar and smashed it, and the red wine poured over the floor. Theseus was a natural wrestler, and he soon had Procrustes at his mercy. With the servant's help he laid him on the bed and tied him down. As Procrustes fitted the bed exactly, there was no need to saw off his legs or use the stretching-gear. Instead he cut off his head with his sword and dragged the body outside for the wolves to devour. Then the servant spread two sheepskins on the floor near the fire, and they lay down and slept. They would not go near the bed.

So it was that Theseus, by his strength and skill and courage, freed the road to Athens of its terrors.

4 THE POISONED CUP

WHEN Theseus reached Athens, the marble temples
and the Royal palace on the hill of the Acropolis were
turning gold in the setting sun. A crowd welcomed
him at the gates and followed him through the streets,
for the servant of Procrustes had run on ahead and
talked of his brave deeds. But Theseus did not linger,
for he was longing to see his father.

The Poisoned Cup

Meanwhile King Aegeus was in the palace at a sacrificial banquet with Medea, his queen. She was a cruel sorceress, dark-eyed, with jewels in her long snaky hair. Many years before, she had killed her two children by a former husband and escaped to Athens in a chariot drawn by dragons. King Aegeus, knowing nothing of her past, had protected her and made her his wife, and she had borne him a son, Medus. Naturally she wanted him to succeed Aegeus as king, and she used her magic powers for this purpose.

When the banquet was over and the guests had gone, she said to Aegeus, 'A young man has just arrived in Athens. His name is Theseus and he is wearing a purple tunic and a soft woollen cloak. I have seen him in my mirror by my magic powers.'

'Why do you tell me this?' said Aegeus.

'Because he is on his way to the palace, sir.'

'Then we must welcome him.'

'He is a criminal and a murderer,' said Medea. 'He has come to claim your throne and will kill anyone who stands in his way.'

'Where is he from, this young man whom you hate so much?'

'From Troezen . . . Why do you tremble, sir, and turn pale? What does Troezen mean to you?'

At this moment the doors opened and a slave came

in. He bowed to King Aegeus and said, 'Sir, a young man named Theseus is here and asks to see you. They say in the city that it was he who cleared the road to Athens of its terrors.'

'Bring him in at once. He is welcome.'

'We will welcome him with *this*!' said Medea, and she pushed before the King a golden cup frothing to the brim with poison. Long ago she had brewed it from the deadly foam that dropped from the jaw of Cerberus, the dog that guarded the Underworld.

Theseus came in and walked boldly up to Aegeus and bowed low. Then he raised his head and looked up for the first time in his life into his father's face. There was such a tumult of feelings in his heart that he could not speak.

Aegeus gazed at him, deep in thought. The youth's noble face and brave bearing touched his heart. It seemed to him that this was no common murderer, but such a one as he would love to call his own son. But because Medea was with him he hid his feelings and said coldly, 'Why have you come to me?'

'Because my father sent me,' said Theseus.

'I have had no message from him,' said Aegeus. 'Who is your father?'

Before Theseus could answer, Medea said, 'My lord, leave these questions till afterwards. The stranger is tired and needs refreshment. This wine will revive him.' And she handed Theseus the golden cup.

The froth had disappeared and the wine was clear and sparkling now. There was about it a fragrance of

roses and a deep restfulness. But Theseus did not drink at once. First he drew his sword and handed it to Aegeus, so that he would recognize the hilt and know his son. Then he raised the cup to his lips.

'Stop!' cried Aegeus, who had seen the serpent on the hilt and now recognized the sword and the sandals, too. And he dashed the cup from his hands, so that the poison spilled on the floor, biting into the marble with a hissing sound.

Then he turned on Medea and with terrible anger cried out, 'This is my son whom you tried to kill. It is you who are the murderer, not he!'

He ordered his guards to arrest her, but he was too late. Muttering her witch songs, she had run to the back of the hall. She wrapped herself in a whirlwind and vanished, and neither her husband nor anyone else ever saw her again.

Still horrified that he had come so near to seeing the murder of his own son, Aegeus embraced him with trembling arms. He asked him about his mother, Aithra, and his grandfather, the King of Troezen. Then he called a meeting of the people in the market-place and presented Theseus to them. 'This is my son Theseus who will rule over you when I am dead,' he said. He lighted fires on the altars and sacrificed many oxen to the gods. The city was gay with feasting and dancing as nobles and commoners rejoiced together and sang of the glorious deeds of Theseus.

5 THE BULL OF MARATHON

YET all was not well in the kingdom of Athens, and
for many years now Aegeus had sat uneasily on his
throne. In the hills outside the city lived a savage
giant-people, ruled by Pallas and his fifty sons, who
declared that Athens belonged to them and that
Aegeus had no right to the throne. Now that Theseus

had arrived they realized that the throne would never be theirs. So they tried to turn the people of Athens against him, and when this failed they plotted to kill him. They lurked in the shadows and at street corners and hurled spears at him when he passed. Twice they wounded him. Aegeus did his best to keep him shut up in the palace, but Theseus escaped all his precautions and went about the city freely.

There was trouble, too, on the great plain of Marathon, where a fire-breathing bull was ravaging the land. No life was safe, and among the many it had killed was Androgeus, the son of King Minos of Crete. The people of Marathon had appealed in vain to Aegeus to help them, but there was no one in the land brave enough to face so terrible a creature— except Theseus. As soon as he heard of it, he decided to go and kill it, and he insisted on going alone.

Pallas now saw his opportunity. Dividing his sons into two parties, he sent one party to attack Theseus as he was leaving the city gates. The other, which he himself led, he ordered to lie in ambush for Theseus in case he escaped the first party. The spot he chose was the top of a pass between two hills on the road to Marathon. At the last moment a herald betrayed the plans to Theseus, who had no difficulty in disposing of both parties. A detachment of the King's guard attacked the party at the gates and killed them all, while Theseus himself, with fifteen chosen soldiers, marched round the hill and attacked the other party from the rear. Only Pallas and two of his sons escaped, but their position was so hopeless now that they had to go on their knees to Aegeus and sue for peace.

Theseus said good-bye to his fifteen warriors and set off alone for Marathon. The sky was blue and cloudless, but during the afternoon the clouds gathered over the mountains and a great storm broke out, with thunder and lightning and heavy rain. Bowing his head to the rain, he ran until he came to a ruined cottage. He kicked open the door and went inside to shelter till the storm had passed. He was wringing out his cloak when suddenly he realized he was not alone. An old woman was lying on a heap of straw, while the rain splashed down on her through holes in the roof. Her wrinkled face was pale and her eyes closed.

'I am sorry,' said Theseus. 'I did not think that any-one lived here. I was looking for shelter from the storm.'

'I never bar the door to travellers,' said the old woman. 'What is your business, stranger?'

'To slay the bull of Marathon.'

'Then you are welcome indeed,' she said, and she

looked at him intently. 'You may rest here tonight, and in the morning I will tell you what to do.'

Theseus had brought some bread and olives with him, which he tried to share with her, but she seemed too ill to eat. So he made her as comfortable as he could, patching up the leaky roof above her and bringing her water to drink. Then he lay down on the floor and went to sleep.

In the morning when he woke she was already up. She had lit a fire in the hearth and was warming goat's milk for him. While he was drinking it, she told him how to deal with the bull. 'When it charges, stand out of the way of its fire and catch it by the horns. Grasp its nostrils with your left hand. It will stop breathing fire and you can force it to the ground.'

She gave him a rope to tie it with, and off he went. He passed through a village and came to the great plain of Marathon, all scorched with fire, and where the smell of burning was strongest he met the bull. Twice it charged him, its hoofs pounding the earth till it trembled like an earthquake. Each time because of the smoke and the fire he could not reach the horns and leapt aside. But the third time he caught hold of them and grasped the nostrils and forced the fierce creature to the ground. As soon as the horns touched the ground it became tame and quiet, and he fastened the rope to its neck and led it away.

As he returned through the village, the people climbed up trees and stood on the rooftops when they

saw the bull. They hailed Theseus as a hero and showered him with leaves and rose petals as he walked through the streets.

'Who is the swiftest runner here?' said Theseus. 'Let him run to Athens to my father King Aegeus and tell him that Theseus is bringing back the bull alive!'

He stopped at the old woman's cottage to give her his joyful news and thank her, but she was lying stiff and cold on the straw and there were people there preparing her for burial. Sadly he gazed at her face, but the look of contentment on it gave him comfort.

'She must be buried with honour,' said Theseus, 'and a shrine built over her grave.'

They burnt down the cottage and buried her where she had lived and where Theseus had sheltered from the storm. Now a shrine marks the place and the country people worship there.

Then Theseus returned in triumph to Athens, dragging the bull through the crowded streets and up the steep hill of the Acropolis till he came to the temple. There he sacrificed it to Athene, goddess of the city, and watched in silence while the flames crackled and the smoke curled up into the sky. Afterwards he was carried shoulder-high to the market-place, where all the people shouted his praises and hailed him as their future king. All day and all night the rejoicing lasted. By noon of the next day they were still singing and dancing, when suddenly, above all the din, a trumpet note rang out, cold and clear and sounding doom.

6 THE SHIP WITH THE BLACK SAIL

IN all the excitement no one had noticed the arrival at Piraeus, the port of Athens, of a strange ship with thirty oars and a black sail. A herald had disembarked and gone straight to the market-place, and it was he who had sounded the trumpet.

'Men of Athens!' he cried. 'Have you forgotten your annual tribute to King Minos of Crete?'

The crowd began to pelt him with stones, till

Theseus held up his hand and stopped them.

'What tribute do you mean?' he asked.

The herald laughed at him. 'Are you an Athenian and have not heard of this? Each year seven young men and seven girls from your city are sent to my master, King Minos, as payment for the crime . . . Do you tell me you know nothing of that crime?' he scoffed. 'Have you not heard of Androgeus and what happened to him?'

'He was the son of King Minos and came to Athens to wrestle at the games,' said Theseus. 'Then he tried his skill against the bull of Marathon. He was no match for it and was killed.'

'Aegeus killed him—by sending him to certain death,' said the herald.

'Why was his death so certain?'

'Go to Marathon and see for yourself.'

'I have been there already and have killed the bull,' said Theseus. 'What did Aegeus have against Androgeus?'

'He was jealous because Androgeus had won all the prizes at the games. Ask Aegeus himself if you doubt my word.'

Then Theseus hurried off to the palace to ask Aegeus if what the herald had said was true. Aegeus hung his head and did not deny it.

'It is true,' he said, and he told Theseus about the Minotaur, a hideous monster with a bull's head and a man's body. He explained that the wife of King Minos was its mother, but to the King it had been a disgrace and a bitter shame. He could not bear to look at it. So under the palace he had had a labyrinth built, a maze of such confusion that no one could find the way out, and he had shut the Minotaur inside.

'It will eat nothing but human flesh,' he added, 'and I am bound by treaty to send each year seven young men and seven girls to feed it. For ten years I have done this. I have paid dearly for my crime.'

'You have paid far too much,' said Theseus. 'But we can end this cruel custom for ever. I shall go myself as one of the victims and I will kill the Minotaur.'

'You must not go, my son,' said Aegeus, trembling. 'I need you here. You must succeed me when I die.'

'Let me kill this monster and I shall be all the worthier of your throne.'

When Aegeus saw it was useless to try to dissuade him, he gave his consent on one condition. 'The ship that takes you to Crete has a black sail,' he said. 'You must carry a white sail with you, too, and when you return, hoist the white one in its place. Then I shall know you are safe. I shall stand on the Acropolis and watch for you each day.'

'I will not forget,' said Theseus, and he embraced his father and returned to the market-place. It was almost empty, for the crowd had gone to the Law Courts for the drawing of lots. When he reached the Courts he saw the fourteen victims, seven boys and seven girls, standing on the steps, their parents and friends in tears beside them.

Theseus broke through the crowd and went up to them and said, 'Do not despair. I will go with you and kill the Minotaur. None of you will die.'

Then an old man said, 'For ten years I have seen the victims go. Not one of them has returned. What chance have you when all the others have failed?'

'I have killed Sinis the pine-bender and Skiron and Procrustes,' said Theseus. 'Why should the Minotaur defeat me? The gods are on our side. We must **not** forget them.'

At once he led his companions to the Dolphin Temple, where he offered the god Apollo an olive branch bound with white wool. Then they went to the harbour. The victim's parents came with them, encouraging them on the way with heroic tales—of how Perseus had killed the sea-monster, and how the infant Heracles had strangled the serpents.

In the harbour the ship was already waiting. The helmsman was standing by the steering-oar; the pilot

at the prow and the thirty oarsmen on their benches were impatient to be off. As the victims embarked, their families and friends followed them up the gangplank, pressing on them food for the voyage, embracing them, clinging to them. And when the pilot cast off the hawsers and the ship drew slowly away, they stretched out their hands to them over the water.

7 KING MINOS OF CRETE

OUTSIDE the harbour the sailors stepped the mast in its box and fixed it with forestays; then hauled the black sail up to the masthead and unfurled it. The north wind filled it, and the ship sped away over the waves. But the victims, huddled together amidships, were cold and lonely as the sea, and the crying gulls above their heads echoed their misery.

36

They sailed past the islands of Aegina and Milos, and on the third day out they sighted far off the cliffs of Crete. A ship came out to meet them.

'She has a golden sail painted with royal dolphins,' said the pilot. 'King Minos himself must be on board.'

The sails of both ships were lowered and the oarsmen took over. The Cretan ship drew alongside. King Minos was standing at the prow, splendid in a golden embroidered cloak that streamed behind him in the breeze. He was a great war-lord and a lover of beautiful things, but he was also vain and given to mockery. When the two ships were close enough for the oarsmen to touch hands, he leapt aboard the Greek ship and asked to see the victims. Trembling with fear, they stood up at the prow, with Theseus beside them. At once a quarrel started. When King Minos saw that there were fifteen and not fourteen of them, he said he would keep one of them as his slave. And he picked out Eriboia, the most beautiful of the girls, and touched her pale cheek with his hand as if she were already his slave. She screamed to Theseus to help her.

Theseus leapt up and stood chin to chin with King Minos and said, 'She is no slave but a noble's daughter. If you touch her again I shall throw you into the sea.'

Never before had anyone spoken to King Minos like that.

'Who are you that dare insult me so?' said King Minos, white with anger.

'I am Theseus, son of King Aegeus.'

'I am the war-lord of Cnossus, king of the islands,' said Minos. 'Immortal Zeus, the king of the gods, is my father.' And stretching out his hands to heaven, he called on Zeus to confirm it with a flash of lightning.

At once the whole face of the sky was split with lightning, and there was a great drum-roll of thunder.

'I have the blood of Poseidon, the sea-god, in my veins,' said Theseus. 'He will give me whatever help I need.'

'Then fetch this,' said King Minos. He threw his gold signet ring into the sea, and it sank at once.

Theseus climbed on to the stern rail and dived into the sea, deep down to the watery halls of Poseidon, the sea-god. And a hundred dolphins, rolling and plunging, brought him to the palace of the Nereids, the daughters of Ocean, who were shining with the splendour of fire. Thetis, the loveliest of the sea nymphs, dressed him in a purple robe and gave him a jewelled crown, her wedding gift from the goddess of love. Meanwhile her sisters swam everywhere to find the golden ring. At last they found it in a cranny of rock and, in front of Poseidon the sea-god, they gave it to Theseus. Then he sped towards the sea-roof, a

long trail of bubbles marking his path back to the
ceiling of light. When he broke the surface, the young
men and girls hauled him eagerly aboard. They were
amazed to see him dressed in a robe even more splendid than King Minos's and not even wet. And when
he handed Minos the golden ring, how they shouted
for joy!

As for Minos, he said not a word, but went back to
his ship and returned to harbour.

8 PRINCESS ARIADNE

IN those days Cnossus was one of the great cities of the world. The nearby port of Heracleion was crowded with shipping, with trading-boats from Egypt and Asia as well as the King's own fleet. People had come from all over the island to see the Athenian strangers. They stared at them as they disembarked and marched up the road to the palace.

And what a palace it was! It spread right over the hill. The halls and galleries and countless rooms were built of huge blocks of stone, framed in cypress wood cut from the forests inland. The wooden columns tapered downwards and were painted russet with blue capitals. There was a grand staircase four stories high, lit by wells of light and thus protected from the hot summer sun and the freezing winter winds. It was far more splendid than the palace of Aegeus.

As Theseus entered the hall at the foot of the staircase, he was startled to see a huge black bull in front of him. It had gold horns and white nostrils, red-rimmed eyes and a fierce mouth. At once he thought of the Minotaur. He drew his sword and waited for the charge.

'The beast is harmless,' laughed King Minos. 'Sheathe your sword.'

Then Theseus saw it was only a painting on the wall, and he too laughed. Every hall he entered was decorated in a similar way. There were pictures of wrestling, boxing, and bullfighting. One of them showed the bull-leaping sport, which was very popular in Crete. As the bull charged, an acrobat seized it by the horns, somersaulted over its back and bounced to the ground. There were also scenes from nature—of flowers and birds and trees and the wild creatures of the hills and seas; pictures of the snake goddess whom they worshipped, of processions and public ceremonies, with the Court ladies sitting round and chatting gaily.

It was the custom for King Minos to entertain his Athenian guests to dinner; they were not shut in the labyrinth till the following day. The cups and dishes were all of solid gold; and the food was lavish and magnificent. Yet Theseus and his companions did not feel hungry. They were haunted by the thought of what lay in store for them next day.

In the middle of the dinner they were puzzled by a sudden growl of thunder that seemed to come from underneath their feet. King Minos was quick to explain it.

'The Minotaur is hungry tonight,' he said. 'Perhaps he has smelt human flesh and cannot wait till morning.'

Then the floor began to tremble and the foundations of the palace quivered and shook, and the wine slopped on to the tables.

'The Minotaur is trying out his paces,' said the King. 'His temper does not improve with waiting. But why should we cut short our entertainment to please him?'

King Minos clearly enjoyed his guests' dismay. Not so his daughter, Ariadne, who admired Theseus's dignity and calm. She asked about his exploits on the road to Athens and listened entranced while he told her about them. She could not bear to think of the miserable death that awaited him and his companions next morning. So she decided to help him.

After the dinner she took Theseus to the Hall of Distaffs, where she did her weaving. The walls were bright with deep blue dolphins and star-fish and spiky sea-urchins painted against a pale blue ground, all lit with a soft light.

'Tomorrow I must wrestle with death,' said Theseus.

'I can help you win and escape safely,' said Ariadne. 'Daedalus, the master craftsman who built the labyrinth, once told me how to find the way out.'

She went to her spindle and picked up a ball of wool.

'As soon as you are inside the door, tie the loose end of the wool to the lintel,' she said, 'and unwind the ball as you go. Do not let it out of your hand or you will never find the way back. When you meet the Minotaur, seize him by the horn and stab him.'

'But we are allowed no weapons,' said Theseus.

'Take this dagger and hide it in your tunic.' She gave it to him; the hilt was of solid gold and the iron point sharp as a needle.

'Tomorrow I shall owe my life to you,' said Theseus. 'Dearest princess, what can I do for you in return?'

'Make me your wife and take me back to Greece,' said Ariadne, and the tears welled up in her eyes. 'I am lonely and unhappy here. The palace is full of soldiers; the talk is of nothing but wars and fighting. And at night the monster bellows so loudly that I cannot sleep. I beg you to take me away.'

'With all my heart,' said Theseus, much moved by her beauty and goodness. And he took her in his arms and kissed her.

9 THE MINOTAUR

NEXT morning the palace guards locked Theseus and his companions in the labyrinth. The huge iron door shut behind them with a clang that echoed through the dark twisting passages, the numberless corridors. And when the last echo had faded, there was a dreadful stillness.

'You have nothing to fear,' said Theseus. 'I shall keep my promise. Wait here till I return.'

He had hidden Ariadne's dagger under his cloak. And to light him on his way he had the jewelled crown which Thetis had given him. He fastened one end of the ball of wool to the lintel above the door and set off into the darkness. Crouching by the door, his companions watched the splash of light on the walls till he turned a corner and vanished; then they listened in the pitch darkness to the echo of his footsteps fading into the distance.

On and on down the endless corridors went Theseus, hour after hour, unwinding the wool as he walked. The stone walls were ice-cold and slimy; they glistened wet in the light of the jewels. Sometimes he stopped to look for signs of the monster, to listen for its footsteps.

He had come to a place where the corridor branched into three when he suddenly heard the sound of heavy breathing. He put down the ball of wool and gripped the hilt of his dagger. He peered round and turned his head slowly while the jewels on his crown, shining like a torch, floodlit the darkness. The Minotaur was lying in the mouth of the third passage, curled up, asleep; the monstrous bull's head with its golden horns and white nostrils was nodding over a human chest. Roused by the light, it opened its eyes, red-rimmed and bloodshot, and for a whole minute blinked at Theseus. Suddenly it let out so great a bellow that it seemed as if the walls had

crumbled and fallen in. High above in the palace Ariadne heard it as she sat weaving in her room, and the distaff fell from her hand. The trees in the forest trembled and a great wave rolled ashore and rocked the ships in harbour.

Then the creature scrambled upright. It lowered its head and, snorting smoke from its fiery nostrils, charged. There was no room for Theseus to step aside, but he remembered what Ariadne had told him to do. He reached up with his left hand, caught hold of a horn and wrenched the head backwards. With his right hand he plunged the dagger into its neck. The beast groaned and slumped forward on top of him, almost smothering him as they fell. For a long moment they rolled and wrestled on the stony floor. Then the Minotaur's muscles went limp and slack and it never moved again.

Theseus struggled to his feet. He picked up what was left of the ball of wool, and winding it up as he went, groped his way back to the mouth of the labyrinth where his companions were waiting. They cheered when they saw him and kissed his hands.

But he silenced them at once, for they were not out of danger yet. 'We must stay here till nightfall, till the guards are sure we are dead,' he told them. 'Then Ariadne will unlock the door and let us out.'

At last they heard the key grate in the lock and the door creak open. The stars were shining as they tiptoed out into the warm night. He called softly to

Ariadne. 'I have killed the Minotaur,' he whispered. He slipped her hand into his and they hurried down to the harbour, with the seven young men and the seven girls behind them.

The ship was waiting. They hoisted sail and cast off their moorings and steered past the sleeping ships. So that King Minos could not pursue them, they scuttled one of the ships in the harbour mouth to block the way out. Then joyfully they made for the open sea.

When Theseus had washed away all trace of the monster's blood, he took Ariadne in his arms and kissed her. With his companions as witnesses, while the wind filled the sail and tugged at the rigging, he made her his wife. And as a pledge that he would love her all his life, he gave her his jewelled crown and set it on her head, where it sparkled in the darkness as brightly as the stars.

10 THE BLACK SAIL

BUT Ariadne never came to Athens with Theseus. The ship had hardly felt the swell of the open sea when a storm blew up. She ran before the wind all night and most of the next day, then put in to the island of Naxos. Leaving the ship at anchor in a quiet bay, Theseus and his companions landed and found shelter in a cave.

The Black Sail

That night while they were all asleep the youngest son of Zeus, Dionysus the wine-god, appeared in the cave. His dark locks were wreathed in vine leaves, and a purple cloak hung from his shoulders. When he saw the sleeping Ariadne, he fell in love with her and was determined to make her his wife and to see that Theseus and his companions sailed away without her. At the touch of his hand on their brows he cruelly wiped away altogether their memory of her.

Ariadne slept on late into the morning, and when she woke she was startled to find that she was alone. Where was the ship? The bay was empty, and the black sail was far away on the horizon. Lonely and terrified, she ran along the shore, cutting her feet on the sharp stones, and weeping. In her despair she cried out to the gods, 'What sort of a man did you give me for a husband? I saved his life, and see how he has treated me.'

Suddenly she heard the sound of flutes and drums and tambourines. Dancing girls came running down the path between the cliffs, each wreathed with ivy and carrying a staff with a pine-cone on the end. Next came a chariot drawn by tigers and lynxes; in it was Dionysus, and fauns and satyrs were running behind him. Joyfully he hailed Ariadne and lifted her into the chariot beside him and comforted her. When she saw that he loved her truly, her loneliness and terror vanished and she was happy again. And the marriage procession danced on. Wherever they passed, the sand turned to grass, and in the crevices between the rocks vines began to grow.

Then Dionysus took the jewelled crown from her head and flung it to the sky, where it faded from their sight. No one ever saw it again by day, but at night it turned to fire, and the jewels that in the labyrinth had lighted Theseus on his way became stars. On cloudless nights you can see them still.

Meanwhile the ship sailed on towards Athens. Theseus sat moodily at the prow and would not speak to anyone, except to urge the sailors to press on home. He drove his thirty oarsmen so hard that they had no time to rest or eat. At last they came in sight of the coast of Attica, and his spirits rose. He longed to see his father again and to be welcomed as a hero.

As soon as they landed, Theseus sent a herald to the city to tell his father of his safe return. Meanwhile the exhausted sailors put what was left of their provisions in a common cooking-pot, boiled them up and ate them ravenously. Theseus would not touch any food until he had first given thanks to the gods for his safe return. He built an altar on the seashore and laid on it an olive branch wreathed with wool and hung with

the season's fruits, for it was harvest-time. Then he made gifts of wine. When he had finished, he saw that the herald had returned from the city and was hovering on the edge of the crowd, not daring to come forward. His herald's staff was twined with garlands.

Theseus went up to him and asked him his news.

'Sir, the people of Athens rejoice in your triumph and greet you with these garlands,' he said as he placed them on Theseus's shoulders.

'Have you no message from my father?'

'He is dead,' said the herald. 'He took his own life. Each day since you sailed he stood on the Acropolis looking out over the sea, impatient for your return. This morning when he saw the black sail he gave you up for dead and flung himself headlong from the rock.'

Then Theseus remembered his promise to Aegeus to hoist the white sail on his return. At once his gladness turned to grief and bitter self-reproach. He would not be comforted. Next day, in deep mourning, he buried his father in a hero's tomb. He would not wear the garlands which the people gave him, but heaped them into the grave. And so that his father's name should not be forgotten, he named the sea that washes the shores of Greece the 'Aegean'.

11 THE WAR WITH THE AMAZONS

THESEUS now became King of Athens. When he had recovered from the shock and sorrow of his father's death, he showed himself a wise and far-sighted ruler. Until now there had been twelve separate communities in Attica, each managing its own affairs and sometimes quarrelling and fighting with each other.

Theseus persuaded them to unite and to accept a single Council Hall and Law Court in Athens. This was no easy task, and he had to visit each clan and family in turn. The common people and the slaves were the first to agree, and the nobles and the land-owners followed when he promised to let them share the government. He gave up his own Royal power but remained commander of the army and chief judge. He sent his heralds all over Greece to invite the people to become citizens of Athens. When they flocked into the city, he divided them into three classes: nobles, farmers, and craftsmen. The duty of the nobles was to look after religion, supply magistrates, and teach the laws; the farmers tilled the soil; and the craftsmen—the biggest class of all—included doctors, soothsayers, heralds, sculptors, builders, and shopkeepers. He also minted money, stamping each coin with the image of a bull, and established festivals and games.

The first trouble that the new State of Athens had to meet came from the Amazons. They were a tribe of women warriors who lived on the shores of the Black Sea at the foot of the mountains and spent their lives fighting. They had brazen bows and shields like half moons. Their clothes were made from the skins of wild beasts, and their helmets and armour from the tough hides of Libyan serpents. One winter they galloped their horses westwards over the frozen sea, across Thrace and Macedonia and down into Greece, conquering and laying waste the land. A farmer came running into the city and reported that they had burnt down his barns and granaries; afterwards he had seen them dancing round their camp fires to the music of pipes, rattling their quivers and stamping on the ground. During the following days more and more country people left their fields and farms and flocked to the city for refuge. But the Amazons swept on, and soon they were camping outside the city walls.

Theseus led out his army against them, and his infantry showered them with javelins. The Amazons were led by their queen Hippolyta, who was a head taller than the others and the bravest of them all. Yelling their hideous war-cry and waving their swords, they quickly scattered the Athenian left wing. On the right wing the soldiers in the front ranks were trampled by the fiery hoofs, but the rest stood firm and tried to drag the Amazons from their horses. After three charges they were forced to retreat. As they went they turned round in their saddles and with deadly accuracy shot their arrows at the Athenians. Among the wounded was Hippolyta. Theseus had dragged her from her horse and fought her hand to hand until she was swept to the ground by a runaway horse and stunned. After the battle he found her lying on the ground, pale-cheeked and with her eyes closed. He had already admired her courage and now he admired her beauty, too. He revived her with water and had her taken to the palace.

Now that they had lost their Queen, the Amazons had no heart to continue fighting, so they made a treaty with Theseus and left the country. But Hippolyta stayed behind and became Theseus's wife. She bore him a son named Hippolytus, a noble youth who loved hunting and was also a great charioteer.

Meanwhile reports of Theseus's wisdom and strength and bravery were spreading all over Greece. They reached Pirithous, King of the Lapiths, who lived in the north at the foot of Mount Olympus. He decided to see for himself if they were true. So he marched south with a large army and raided Attica. On the great plain of Marathon, which borders the eastern coast, he found a herd of cattle grazing and drove them away. But when he heard that Theseus and his army were hot on his trail, he did not run away; he turned back to meet them.

Theseus's army, mostly infantry, was ranged along a hill and had the advantage of the slope. The army of Pirithous was twice as big and all his soldiers were

mounted. Undismayed, Theseus rode quietly forward on his white horse with his sword drawn. He did not stop until he was within hailing distance of Pirithous. He was going to give the signal for the charge, but he could not do it. Admiration for his enemy's noble looks and bearing overcame him. He could see no trace of fear in the King's eyes, and his limbs were so strong that they might have been carved out of the living rock. Pirithous felt the same about Theseus. Sheathing his sword and spurring his black horse forward, he rode up to Theseus and clasped him by the hand.

'Noble Theseus,' he said, 'I did wrong to raid your country and steal your cattle. I can wish you nothing but good and will gladly submit to any penalty you like to name.'

'The penalty,' said Theseus, 'is that you swear an oath of everlasting friendship with me. And you must ride with me to Athens, where we shall feast and rejoice together.'

Pirithous swore his oath, and they rode away to Athens, each delighting in the companionship of the other.

12 HELEN

Soon after his return north from Athens, Pirithous married a wife named Hippodamia. Theseus was one of the wedding guests; so were the Centaurs, half men, half horses, who lived on the Lapith borders and were related to the bride. Unfortunately they turned the feast into a drunken brawl, and Theseus, out of loyalty to his friend, became involved in a long feud with them. With the help of Heracles he finally drove them away from their ancient hunting-grounds on Mount Pelion and forced them farther inland. Hippodamia died soon afterwards, and Theseus had hardly returned from the war with the Centaurs when he heard that his own wife, Hippolyta, had died, too.

The days of happiness and triumph for Theseus were now over, and the rest of his life was darkened by sadness and misfortune, for much of which he was himself to blame.

At this time Helen of Troy was only a child of twelve. But she was already so beautiful that Theseus was determined to marry her when she grew up. So he and Pirithous went to Sparta where she lived, seized her while she was dancing in the temple of Artemis and galloped off with her. Aithra, the mother of Theseus, was now living in Athens and they handed Helen over to her and asked her to look after her till she was ready for marriage. Aithra soon grew very fond of Helen and treated her as if she were her own child.

One day, when she was teaching her to weave, she heard a scuffle in the passage outside. The door burst open and in rushed two young men with drawn swords. Aithra stood in front of the child, trying to shield her, but Helen showed no fear of the young men and with a cry of joy ran to greet them. They were her brothers, Castor and Pollux. Castor threw down his sword and hugged her, but Pollux stood facing the door, ready to fight his way out. He had not long to wait before Theseus came in, followed by Pirithous and most of the palace guard.

Pollux lunged at Theseus, who found it easy to ward off the blow and knock the boy's sword from his hand. Pirithous put his foot on Castor's sword before he could touch it. The two boys tried to continue the fight with their fists, but they were quickly overpowered and would have been killed had not Theseus intervened.

'Sir, we are Helen's brothers and have come to claim her back,' said Castor.

'You had no right to seize her,' said Pollux. 'Our cause is just.'

For a minute Theseus was silent. Then he turned to Helen and said, 'Is it true that these men are your brothers?'

'It is true, sir.'

'And you wish to go back home with them?'

'I do, sir.'

'Has my mother Aithra not treated you well?'

'My own mother could not have been kinder,' said Helen.

'Then why do you wish to go?'

'Because you forced me to come against my will. I am a stranger here and I belong to my own family, not to you.'

'When you are older you may be glad to return,' said Theseus.

'I could never grow to love you, sir. You are too stern,' said Helen.

There was a gasp of astonishment, for no one in the

palace had ever been so outspoken to Theseus before. But Theseus only smiled. He admired Helen for her calm bravery and her brothers for their courage.

'You have acted nobly and are free to take her home,' said Theseus.

Helen ran forward and knelt and kissed his hand. But Pirithous was angry and indignant.

'Sir, does it mean nothing to you that these young men have killed two of your guards?' he said hotly. 'Wars have been started for less than this. With your army you could soon bring Sparta to her knees.'

'The gods would not bless our victory,' said Theseus. 'I did wrong to seize Helen, and I cannot fight for an unjust cause.'

And he let the brothers go back in peace to their own home, taking Helen with them.

13 THE KINGDOM OF THE DEAD

SOON afterwards Pirithous was talking to Theseus about women and marriage. 'There is one I know who is more beautiful than Helen could ever be,' he said. 'Her name is Persephone, Queen of the Underworld.'

'Then why not visit the Underworld and demand her as your bride?' said Theseus jokingly.

'That is what I mean to do,' said Pirithous. 'The oracle of Zeus has told me she is the noblest of his daughters.'

Theseus never intended his suggestion to be taken seriously. But he had already promised, in return for his friend's support in fetching Helen, to help him find a bride for himself. Now Pirithous bound him to his oath, and Theseus dared not break it.

The Underworld was the kingdom of the dead, from which only gods and heroes ever returned. A sloping path, shaded by deadly yew-trees, led down to it. The marshy River Styx, whose banks were choked with reeds, flowed along the border, and Charon the ferryman took all the dead over in his boat. But Theseus and Pirithous did not go this way. They chose the back way and entered by a secret cavern deep in the Caucasus Mountains, by the shores of the Black Sea. It was called the Cavern of Hades and was bitterly cold, and so dark that they needed torches. For safety they carried their swords as well. Down and down the long tunnel of gloom they went. Presently they heard the sound of barking. At the end of the tunnel they turned a corner, and the darkness faded into twilight, and suddenly a huge three-headed hound stood in their path. It was Cerberus, the guardian of the gates of hell. Each head had a mane of biting snakes, and snakes instead of hair hung from his back. He could swallow anything with his three mouths. He greeted the dead by wagging his tail like a good sheepdog. But he ate all the living strangers he could catch, for he liked his meat raw. With a savage growl he rushed at the two kings, lashing the air with his barbed tail. But he was chained to a stake, and as the links tautened they both managed to avoid his cruel jaws.

Before them stretched the Underworld, a landscape of grey upon grey, merging into heaviest black. There was no colour or brightness at all. They walked across fields of asphodel, flowers that looked like blossoms of grey mist, over which drifted the ghosts of the dead, bloodless spirits without body or bone. If they ventured too near, the ghosts ran away with a soft twittering and whirring sound. They passed the Elysian fields, which were more beautiful than any fields on earth. The leaves on the trees and hedges were black, and the ground was thick with black hyacinths—a hundred blooms springing from a single root and filling the air with fragrance.

At last they came to the palace of a thousand gates where Hades was King and welcomed the newly dead. The palace was roofless, for there was no sun, rain or wind in the Underworld. The two kings

knocked on the gates, which opened soundlessly. They passed into a court of playing fountains and entered a grove of cypress-trees that grew not far from the palace walls. Here, on ebony thrones, sat King Hades and his Queen Persephone. It was their favourite spot, for there was no wall in front of them and they could look out over half their kingdom and watch the rivers that all the dead must cross when they first arrived.

'What is your errand?' said King Hades.

'I have come in search of a wife,' said Pirithous, who always went straight to the point.

'Then you have come to a strange place, for only the shades live here,' said Hades. 'Can you find no lady on earth to please you?'

'No one to compare in beauty with the lady of my choice.'

'What is her name?' said Hades.

'Persephone,' said Pirithous, and he took from his wallet a narcissus, Persephone's favourite flower, which she loved more than lilies or violets, and he handed it to her.

Her pale hands accepted it, but she did not smile or speak.

'And what does your companion want?' asked Hades, apparently unmoved by this impudent request.

'Nothing, sir, except permission to stand by my friend,' said Theseus.

'Then you will need to be very patient,' said Hades, and Theseus wondered what he meant. 'You must both be tired after your long journey. There are two rocks in my garden. Sit down on them and rest.'

The two friends walked unsuspectingly across the garden to the rocky seats they had been offered.

Theseus was the first to sit down. At once he felt his limbs stiffen. He tried to get up, but he could not, because the rock had become part of his flesh. He cried out to his friend to warn him not to sit down. Pirithous was standing by the rock, irresolute, wondering what to do, when a hundred snakes oozed from a crack in the earth. They hissed and spat at him and drove him against the rock, so that he could not help sitting down. Now he, too, was stuck and unable to move. Then the three winged Furies swooped down on them, lowing like cattle. Their skins were black, their clothes were grey, and they had hissing snakes for hair. As they circled above the two kings, they breathed on them with their foul breath and beat them with brass-studded whips.

Hades watched them, smiling grimly. And beside him Persephone was tearing off one by one the petals from her flower and crushing the green stalk under heel. She did not smile at all.

14 THE RESCUE

So Theseus came to the Underworld, where everything was strange to him. There was no cockcrow to greet the dawn, no singing of birds, no wind to stir the branches of the trees, no sound but the whirring of ghosts and the far-away barking of Cerberus. Fixed to his rocky seat, he watched all the traffic of the

Underworld. He could see in the distance the River Styx, and on its sluggish, poisonous waters old Charon's boat with its cargo of newly dead. He watched them step ashore into the country of dreams and, led by Hermes with his golden rod, drift over the cold waste to Lethe, the river of forgetfulness. And as they crossed they trailed their hands in the stream and sipped its waters. By the time they had reached the other side, they could remember nothing of their lives on earth. They belonged now to the innumerable nation of the dead.

Then King Hades, commander of souls and host to many guests, went out to meet them, driving in his black chariot drawn by black horses with silent hoofs. The spirits of the blessed he sent to the Elysian fields, to live there in happiness for ever, but the damned endured eternal torment for their crimes. Among these was Tantalus, who had been here many years. Tortured by hunger and thirst, he could not reach the fruit that hung from the bough overhead or the water that flowed past his lips. Another was Sisyphus, for ever pushing his rock uphill; whenever it topped the summit, it rolled down again to the plain. Another was Ixion, chained throughout eternity to a burning, whirling wheel. To Pirithous this was the cruellest sight of all, for Ixion was his father. And once

Theseus saw his own father Aegeus wandering pale and listless through the palace courts. He called out to him and stretched out his arms. But Aegeus did not know him; he glanced at him with frightened, empty eyes, and then with a whirring sound drifted on.

Many years passed. Then one day Theseus heard something he had not heard since he left the earth— the sound of human laughter. It was louder than the three barking mouths of Cerberus and could come from nobody but Heracles. He was wearing his lion-skin and carried his sword and club. He was ten feet high and very strong, and the muscles on his arm were like a rippling river. Of all the heroes Theseus admired him most.

'Heracles!' he called. 'I am Theseus, King of Athens. Do you remember me?'

Heracles ran to him and held out both hands in welcome. 'We have not met since we fought the Centaurs together. This is a strange place to find you. Why did you come here?'

Theseus told him the reason.

'A rash venture,' said Heracles, 'and I see that you have suffered for it. But perhaps my own venture is no less rash than yours. The King of Argos has sent me to capture Cerberus. Of the twelve labours he gave me to do, this is the last and by no means the lightest. I had to fight my way in with my sword. When I came to the River Styx, Charon refused to row me across because I had no money. He sneered at me and said, "The dead keep a coin under their tongues to pay their passage. What have you brought?" "A scowl," I said, and I treated him to one of my fiercest. He didn't dare refuse again. But it's a wonder I didn't drown in that ferry of his. It's only sewn together from pieces of bark, and under my weight the rim was level with the water.'

By now Persephone and King Hades had seen him and were coming towards him. Persephone had known Heracles on earth before Hades had made her his queen. She now greeted him like a brother. He told her why he had come to the Underworld and asked if he might take Cerberus back with him.

'I will ask my lord,' said Persephone.

'The hound is yours, Heracles, if you can master him,' said King Hades. 'But you must promise to use no weapon—no club, no sword, no arrows.'

Heracles promised. Then he turned to Persephone and asked her if she could yet forgive his friend Theseus his folly. Persephone agreed at once, for she had always admired Heracles and was willing to please him.

'May he return to the world of men?'

'I will ask my lord,' said Persephone.

'Theseus is fixed to his rock for ever, and not even your strength, Heracles, can move him,' said King Hades. But he added, 'You may try to release him if you wish.'

'I will try anything for a friend,' said Heracles.

He put down his club. Then he took hold of his friend's hands, placed his right foot against the rock and tugged with all his might. Three times he tugged, and at the third time wrenched him free. Stiff-limbed and wincing with pain, Theseus stood up. When Heracles saw that his friend had left some of his skin behind, he called it jokingly the price of his freedom.

He next tried to do the same for Pirithous. The snakes that had twined themselves round the King's legs spat and hissed at him, but he managed to uncoil them and break their backs with his club. But when he seized Pirithous by the hands, King Hades raised his arm and in a terrible voice cried out to him to stop. And to show his displeasure he sent an earthquake that shook his whole kingdom.

Heracles knew better than to persist. He bowed low to King Hades and Persephone and quickly led Theseus away.

So it was that Theseus was rescued, but Pirithous stayed behind to suffer torment for ever.

15 THE FIGHT WITH CERBERUS

THE loss of his friend Pirithous saddened Theseus, but he could not change the will of the gods. As they hastened on through the twilight of the Underworld, Heracles talked to him about his adventures, now and then pausing to stuff a barley cake in his mouth. He liked to carry food with him, as his huge energy made him always hungry.

'When Charon landed me from the Styx,' he said, 'the ghosts were so frightened that they ran away from me, squeaking and twittering like bats. But two of them stood firm. The first was the Gorgon Medusa. I drew my sword, but Hermes told me it was useless against her—I could not hurt the air. The other ghost was my old enemy Meleager, dressed in full armour. He smiled and said that I had nothing to fear from the dead, and we were friends at once. But imagine—a ghost in full armour!' and he laughed aloud.

Theseus paused in the Elysian fields to pluck leaves from a black-leaf poplar, and with these he wove a wreath for Heracles and put it round his brows.

They crossed the cold, desolate waste, and at last they reached the far fringe of the Underworld, the mouth of the gloomy tunnel where Cerberus was chained. They spoke in whispers now, for they did not want Cerberus to hear them. They hid behind the rocks, slinking from one to the other and guided by the barks. And suddenly they saw him, lying by his stake. Was the hound asleep? Two heads were resting on his paws, but the third was alert, the sullen eyes suspicious. He saw the strangers and knew at once that they were no spirits to greet with wagging tail. Then all of him awoke and he gave three yelps and charged.

They stood out of his reach and waited till the chain that tethered him pulled him up short and tautened with a clang. He pawed the air, and the tunnel under the mountain echoed and re-echoed to his barking. He went back and charged again, and, as the chain tautened, the stake shuddered in the ground. If it failed to hold, what chance had bare hands against three heads of snarling fangs?

But Heracles was ready and did not flinch. The hound had three heads, which branched from a single throat—and there he saw his chance. At the third charge, at the very moment that the chain checked him, Heracles sprang up at his throat and grappled. He pressed with all his strength and held the snapping fangs clear. The snakes on the three heads writhed and hissed. The brute lashed at him with his barbed tail, but the lion's skin he wore protected him from harm. The tighter his fingers gripped, the feebler grew the lashing. The hound began to choke, slumped and lay still. The only sound was the hissing of the snakes, and it was like the hissing of water on red-hot iron.

Heracles stood back, gasping for breath, his huge chest heaving and panting from the labour like a giant bellows. The sweat ran in rivers down his face and along his arms. A strange thing had happened to the wreath on his head. The outer leaves of the wreath were still black, but the inner leaves were bleached white by his sweat. Since that day the white poplar, whose leaves are white underneath when the wind turns them up, has been sacred to Heracles.

'I have not killed the brute, but I have broken his spirit,' said Heracles. 'He will know who is master when he wakes.'

But when Cerberus recovered, he was not as obedient as Heracles had expected. He soon regained some of his strength and struggled to break free. But Heracles snapped the chain in two and used it as a lead; then urged the hound forward into the mouth of the dark tunnel that led back to the world of men. With his huge strength he half dragged him, half carried him all the way, while Theseus stood ready to club his three snouts if he disobeyed. They moved quickly in the darkness, for the eyes of Cerberus were as bright as the sparks that a blacksmith strikes from iron when the anvil rings to his blows, and they lit the way. At last, high above them, they saw a pinprick of light. It grew bigger as they struggled towards it. It was the mouth of the secret cavern by which Theseus had entered long ago. And now he was

standing there with his friend and rescuer at the foot
of the Caucasus Mountains by the shore of the Black
Sea. The rocks and overhanging trees, chilled by the
icy breath of the Underworld, were white with

frost. The strong sunlight made both men half close
their eyes till they got used to it again. But Cerberus
had only known twilight and darkness and had never
seen the sun before. For him the white glare was

blinding, and he bounded painfully away along the bleak shore, with Heracles close on his heels. His three mouths were barking and yelping, the snakes on his mane and back were hissing, and wherever his saliva fell a poisonous plant sprang up.

Theseus watched them till they were out of sight and hearing. He was still grieving for his friend Pirithous and very tired, and he lay down in the mouth of the cave and slept.

16 THE GOLDEN EAGLE

ALL the rest of the day and all night he slept, and in the morning he woke refreshed. Full of hope and happy expectation, he set off on the long road to Athens. He could only walk slowly, for his tortures had greatly weakened him, and it was many weeks before he arrived home.

The first thing he did was to build an altar sacred to Heracles his rescuer. Then he went into the market-place and told the crowd who he was. But they only laughed at him and said that Theseus had been dead for many years. So he showed them his sword and the carving of the serpent on the hilt. Most of them refused to accept this as proof. But there were a few old men who had seen it before and recognized in the creased and worn face before them a faint likeness to their king and hero. He asked after his mother, Aithra, and they told him that she had long ago been carried away to Sparta as a slave and no one knew if she were alive or dead. Next they took him to the palace, where Menestheus was now king. He had seized the throne and by bribery and terror made his position safe, undoing all the good that Theseus had done. Menestheus refused to see him and ordered the palace guard to kill him. But Theseus escaped and went into hiding. Gradually he gathered friends about him, but his attempts to regain the throne failed and all ended in strife and trouble.

In despair he sailed for Crete, where the new King, Deucalion, had promised him refuge. As the ship sailed away from Piraeus, he looked across the water towards Athens and solemnly cursed his people.

A storm blew the ship off her course, and she

drifted at the mercy of wind and wave far up the Aegean Sea to the island of Scyros, where Lycomedes, a close friend of Menestheus, was King. Theseus had inherited an estate on the island, and he now asked Lycomedes if he might settle there in peace. Lycomedes agreed and received him with all the ceremony and honour due to a great hero. He gave a banquet for him, then took him up a mountain to show him the boundaries of his estate. From this climb Lycomedes returned alone. He said that his guest had drunk too much at the banquet and had slipped and fallen to his death. The tale was false. He had treacherously murdered Theseus by pushing him over a precipice.

In due course news of his death reached Athens, but no one mourned him. Six hundred years later, when the Athenians fought the Persians at Marathon, it was said that his spirit in full armour rose from the earth and led them to victory. After the battle the priestess of Delphi gave orders that the bones of Theseus should be brought home to Athens for burial. This was a difficult task, for the people of Scyros were wild and barbarous and refused to say where the grave was. Even when the Athenian admiral Cimon captured the island, they still refused, and Cimon was left to search for it alone.

Suddenly he saw a golden eagle swoop down on to a hilltop and begin to tear up the earth with its talons. He took this as a sign from heaven and ran to fetch a spade. He enlarged the hole which the eagle had made and soon struck the stone coffin of a man of extraordinary size. Inside it he found a skeleton and beside it a bronze lance and a sword. It was the same sword that Theseus had found in his youth under the rock and which he had kept all his life.

Cimon had these precious relics carried to his flagship and he brought them home in triumph to Athens, where they were buried with great honour. A temple was built above the grave and decorated with sculptures and paintings to celebrate the hero's great deeds. It was called the Sanctuary of Theseus and became a refuge for runaway slaves and all who were poor or oppressed, for Theseus had always been their champion.